Before you read, can you match the words with the pictures?

1. chair

2. bowl

3. porridge

4. bear

5. girl

6. store

7. table

8. mother

a 

b 

c 

d 

e 

f 

g 

h 

Listen, read, and circle.

Pages 2~3

This is the story of Goldilocks and three girls. / **bears.**

Goldilocks is a little / big girl.

She lives / makes with her mother.

One day her mother says, "Goldilocks, go to the house. / store.

Buy two muffins and some bread." / chairs."

Goldilocks says, / gets, "OK."

Her mother says, "Be happy. / careful.

Don't go through / for the forest."

But Goldilocks walks through the forest. / store.

She isn't angry. / afraid.

Answer the questions.

1. Goldilocks lives with her __________.

   a. ☑ mother   b. ☐ father   c. ☐ bear

2. Goldilocks walks through the __________.

   a. ☐ bridge   b. ☐ house   c. ☐ forest

3. In the bears' house, there are __________ chairs.

   a. ☐ two   b. ☐ three   c. ☐ four

4. There is a __________ bed for Baby bear.

   a. ☐ big   b. ☐ smaller   c. ☐ little

5. The three bears eat the __________.

   a. ☐ bread   b. ☐ cake   c. ☐ porridge

6. Father bear says, "This porridge is __________."

   a. ☐ cold   b. ☐ hot   c. ☐ just right

Listen, read, and circle.

Pages 6~7

There are three beds in the [house: / **bedroom:**]

a big [chair / bed] for Father bear,

a smaller bed for [Mother / Father] bear,

and a [little / big] bed for Baby bear.

The three bears [have / sit] at the table.

They [eat / see] the porridge. The porridge is too [small. / hot.]

[Father / Mother] bear says, "This porridge is hot!"

Mother bear says, "The porridge is [too / very] hot.

We can't eat it now. Let's [have / go] for a walk."

So the three bears go for a [cry / walk] in the forest.

What do they say?

a. Is anyone home?

b. This porridge is hot!

c. Just right!

d. My bowl is empty!

e. Let's go for a walk.

Complete the sentences with these words.

bowls   sits   eats   ~~walks~~   angry   come

1. Goldilocks __walks__ through the forest.

2. Goldilocks sees three __________ of porridge on the table.

3. Goldilocks __________ the porridge in the little bowl.

4. Goldilocks __________ in the big chair.

5. The three bears __________ home.

6. Baby bear is __________.

Listen, read, and circle.

Pages 12~13

Goldilocks is [right. / (tired.)] She [walks / sees] up the stairs.

She sees three [beds. / bears.] She [sleeps / makes] in the big bed.

She says, "Too [low!" / high!"]

She sleeps [in / out] the smaller bed.

She [says, / knocks,] "Still too high!"

She sleeps in the [small / little] bed.

She says, "Just [right!" / afraid!"]

Just then the three bears [come / jump] home.

The little bowl is [empty. / porridge.]

Baby bear says, "My porridge! My [bed / bowl] is empty!"

Baby bear is [careful. / angry.]

What do they say?

a. Come back and play with me.

b. Somebody is in my bed!

c. Don't be afraid. We don't want to eat you.

d. Who are you?

e. Look! It is broken!

Match the pictures to the sentences.

a. Father bear makes a new chair.

b. Mother bear makes new porridge.

c. Goldilocks wakes up. She sees the three bears.

d. Baby bear is happy to have a new chair.

e. Goldilocks runs all the way home.

f. Goldilocks is afraid. She gets up quickly.

Put the words in the correct order.

1. the   This   bears'   is   house   .

   This is the bears' house.

2. knocks   door   the   She   on   .

3. home   anyone   Is   ?

4. the   in   eats   She   porridge   the   bowl   big   .

5. Goldilocks   three   sees   chairs   .

6. chair   little   in   sits   the   She   .

Fill in the gaps.

right   hard   hot   big   ~~little~~   empty

1. Goldilocks is a __little__ girl.

2. There is a __________ bed for Father bear.

3. Father bear says, "This porridge is __________."

4. Goldilocks says, "This porridge is just __________."

5. Goldilocks says, "This chair is too __________."

6. Baby bear says, "My bowl is __________!"

Are these sentences true or false?

1. Goldilocks is a little girl.

   ☑ True   ☐ False

2. Goldilocks lives with her father.

   ☐ True   ☐ False

3. The three bears live in the forest.

   ☐ True   ☐ False

4. Goldilocks breaks Baby bear's chair.

   ☐ True   ☐ False

5. The smaller chair is too soft for Goldilocks.

   ☐ True   ☐ False

6. The big bed is too low for Goldilocks.

   ☐ True   ☐ False

7. Father bear makes new porridge for Baby bear.

   ☐ True   ☐ False

Write the words.

girl   ~~bedroom~~   forest   sit   bear
bowl   mother   table   chair

1

b e d r o o m

2

_ _ _ _ _

3

_ _ _ _

4

_ _ _ _ _ _

5

_ _ _

6

_ _ _ _

7

_ _ _ _ _ _

8

_ _ _ _ _

9

_ _ _ _

Number the sentences and tell the story.

☐ Goldilocks sees three bowls of porridge on the table.

☐ Goldilocks walks through the forest. She sees a house.

☐ The three bears come home. The little bowl is empty. Baby bear is angry.

☐ Goldilocks runs all the way home. The three bears never see Goldilocks again.

[1] The three bears go for a walk in the forest.

☐ Goldilocks eats the porridge in the little bowl.

Crossword.

1
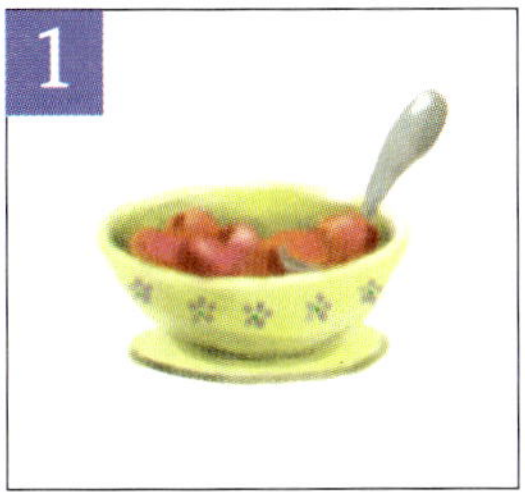

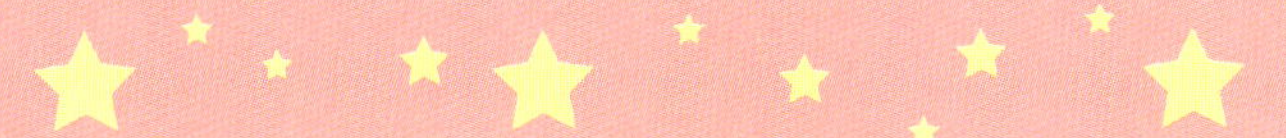

2
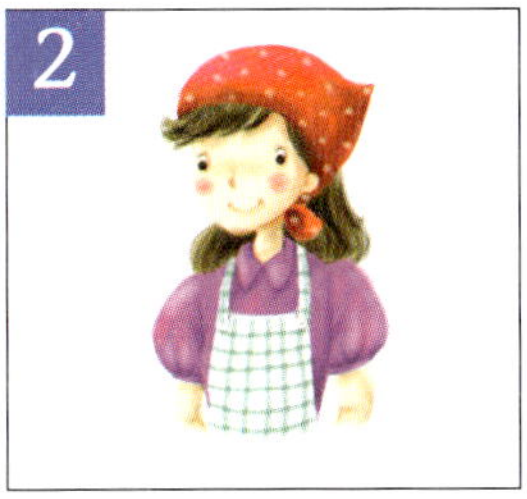

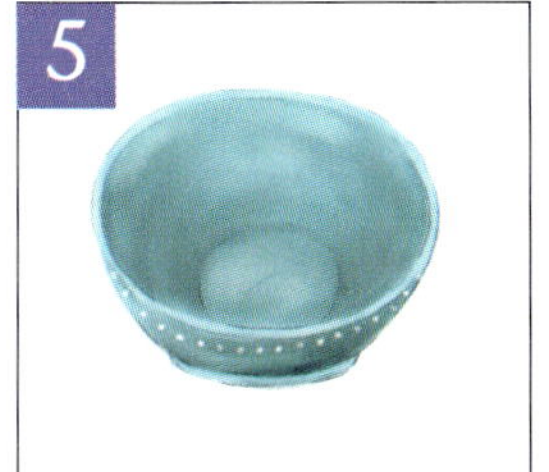

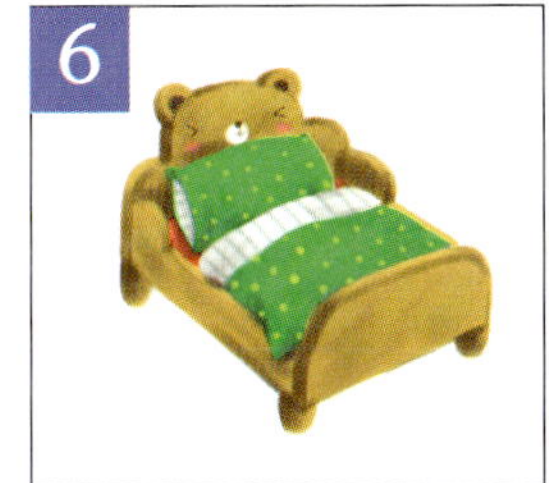

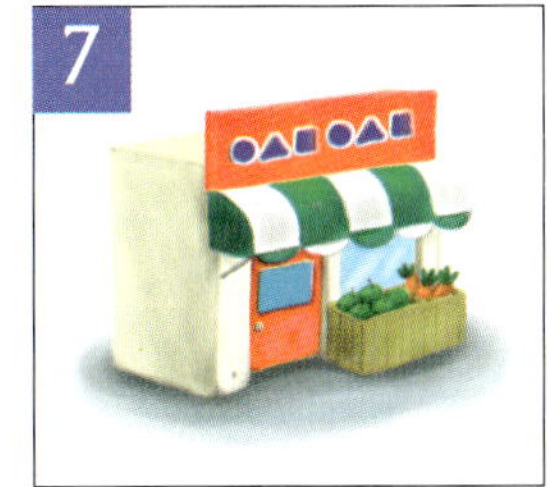

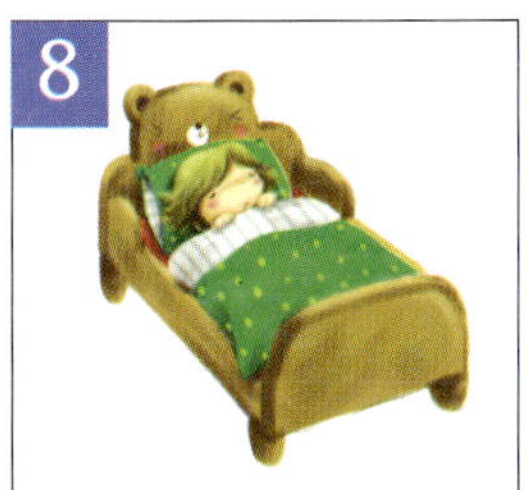

3
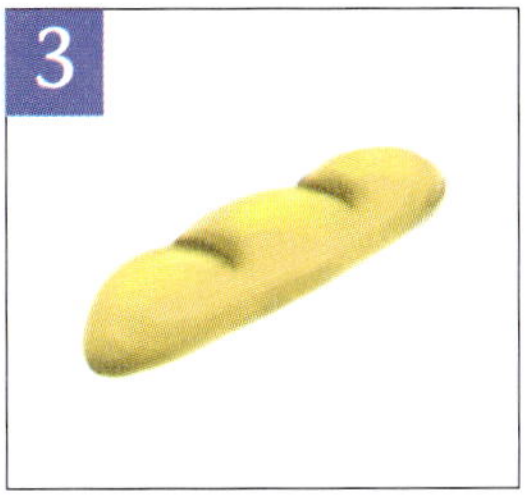

4
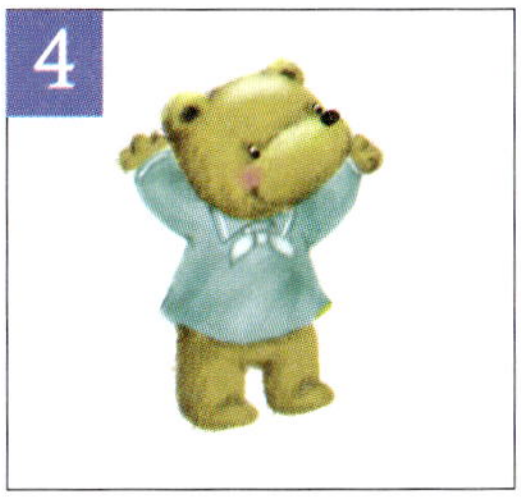

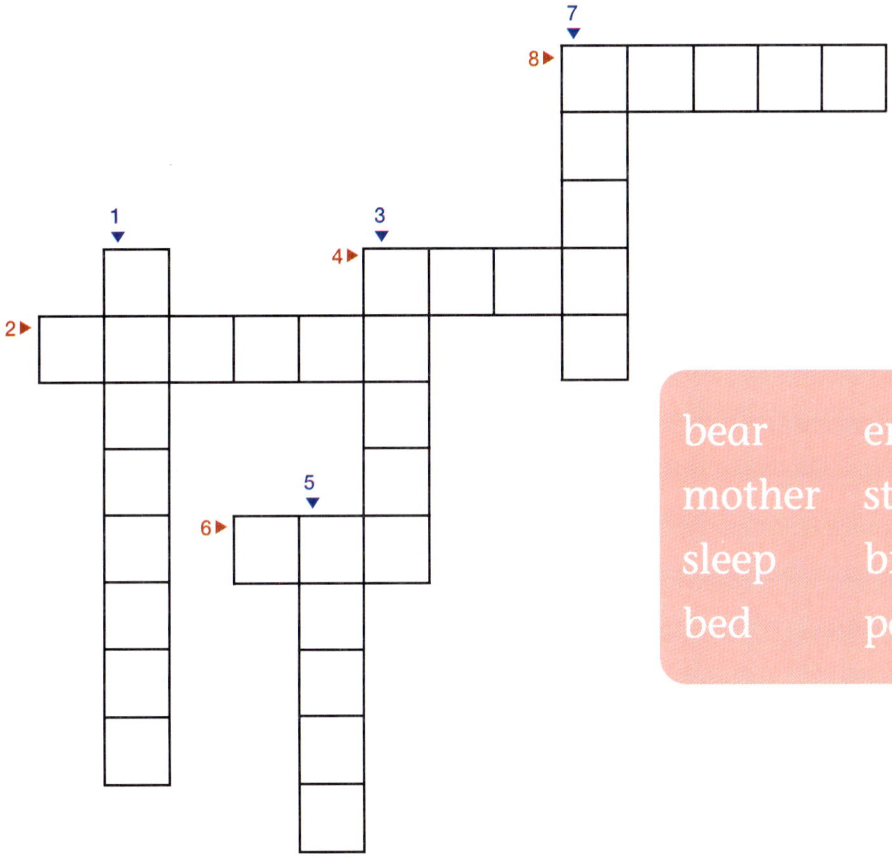

bear	empty
mother	store
sleep	bread
bed	porridge

5

6

7

8

Answer the questions.

1. Who goes to the store?
   - a. ☐ Goldilocks' mother
   - b. ☐ the three bears
   - c. ☑ Goldilocks

2. Who lives in the forest?
   - a. ☐ the birds
   - b. ☐ the three bears
   - c. ☐ Goldilocks

3. Goldilocks eats the porridge in the __________ bowl.
   - a. ☐ little
   - b. ☐ big
   - c. ☐ smaller

4. The big chair is too hard for __________.
   - a. ☐ Goldilocks
   - b. ☐ Father bear
   - c. ☐ Mother bear

5. Goldilocks sleeps in the __________ bed.
   - a. ☐ big
   - b. ☐ smaller
   - c. ☐ little

6. Goldilocks __________ all the way home.
   - a. ☐ runs
   - b. ☐ walks
   - c. ☐ jumps